ADVICE AND INSTRUCTIONS ON COMPLETING THIS TEST

Association of Quality Education Practice TEST NUMBER 1
Common Entrance Assessment Practice Paper

1. **There are 58 questions in this test.**
2. **Start at question 1 and work your way to question 55.**
3. **If you are unable to complete a question leave it and go to the next one.**
4. **Do not think about the question you have just left as this wastes time.**
5. **If you change an answer make sure the change is clear.**
6. **You may do any rough work on the test paper or on another piece of paper.**
7. **This test should take approximately 60 minutes.**
8. **When you have finished this test mark it with an adult.**
9. **An adult may be able to explain any questions you do not understand.**

Whilst the content of this test is believed to be true and accurate at the time of publishing, neither the authors nor the publishers can accept any legal responsibility or liability for any errors or omissions that may have been made. If, however, you do find any errors please contact us at smcconkey@learningtogether.co.uk so that we can correct them.

Do not write in this column

SPRING

Majestic cherry blossom swaying
Like candy floss in the breeze.
Buzzy bumble bees collecting
Nectar from the flowers of baby pink.
The buttercup, daffodil,
Stands proudly in the tub
Prickly holly with blood red berries
Buds appearing on wrinkled branches
Birds sing a sweet lullaby
Everything still barely moving
Except for the gentle whistle of the wind.
By Jill McConkey

1. The poet uses the word **'majestic'**.
Which word means the same or almost the same as **'majestic'** ?
Tick ✓ the best answer.

Regal ☐

Loyal ☐

Magic ☐

Tall ☐

2. What do bees collect from the flowers?

(____)

3. The poet uses the phrase **'Buds appearing on wrinkled branches'.**
What does she mean by this ?
Tick ✓ the best answer.

Buds are growing on an old lady ☐

The branches are coming to life after winter ☐

The branches have winkled skin ☐

The poet has wrinkled skin ☐

(3)

Do not write in this column	

4. Which word below best describes the **wind** in the poem ?
Tick ✓ the best answer.

Hurricane ☐

Gusty ☐

Gentle ☐

Stormy ☐

5. Circle the **verb** in this sentence from the poem

Stands proudly in the tub

6. Circle the **adjective** in this sentence from the poem.

Birds sing a sweet lullaby

7. "Branches" is a **plural** word.
What is the **plural** of these words ?

Salmon (________________________________)

Cherry (________________________________)

Chair (________________________________)

(4)

Do not write in this column

Look at this diagram that is not drawn to scale.

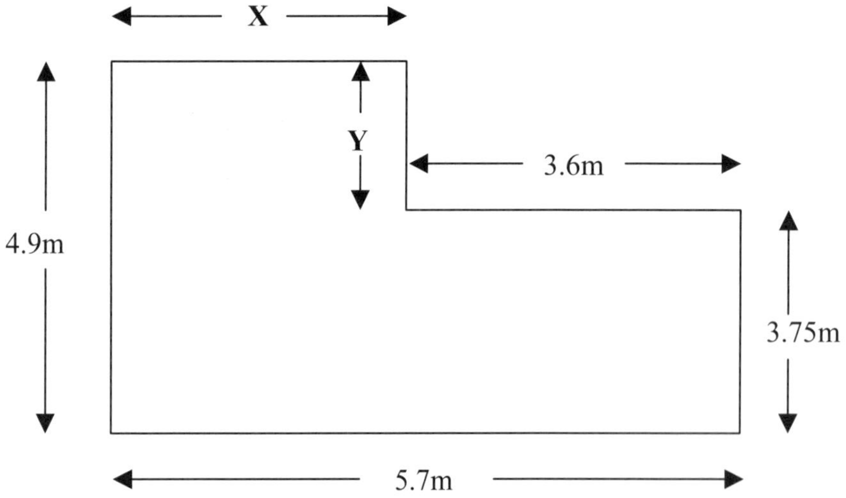

X
Y
3.6m
4.9m
3.75m
5.7m

8. What is the length at X ? (________________m)

9. What is the length at Y ? (________________m)

10. Mark walks around the perimeter of this shape. How far does he walk ?

(________________m)

What is the cost of the following items?

11. 1kgs of sweets at 75p for 200g ? (___£________________)

12. 6.5 litres of petrol at 90p per litre ? (___£________________)

13. ¾ metre of material at £16.00 per metre ? (___£________________)

14. Eggs can be packed into boxes that hold six eggs each.
How many boxes are needed to pack 58 eggs ?

(____________boxes___)

(7)

Do not write in this column

Look at this number machine. It divides a number by 4 and then adds 8 to the answer.
Using this number machine complete the table below.

Number in → Divide by 4 → Add 8 → Number out

Question Number	Number In	Number Out
15	4	
16		24
17		60
18	5	

4/4/09 Day One On Our First Winter Ski Trip.

The alarm clock rang at 7.30 and with great excitement we got ready to go to the airport. We didn't really need the alarm clock as both me and my two brothers had hardly slept all night – with excitement and anticipation.

"Hurry up or we'll be late," shouted our mother. After a swift breakfast we jumped into the car and we were off.
The boredom of an airport queue was soon forgotten when our flight landed at Nice airport. Two small minibuses were waiting to take both families to the ski resort high in the French Alps and about 90 kilometres from the French airport in Nice.

It was a windy and slow journey and my baby brother was nearly sick! When we arrived at our apartment there was snow everywhere – it was at least 3 metres deep and still falling. Our apartment was clean and compact. Quickly we unpacked because, although it was late afternoon, daddy insisted we all got fitted for our ski boots. Mark my older brother was very helpful in the ski shop and knew what to do because he had skied before with his school.

I didn't realise that skis and boots were so heavy and we had to carry them all the way back to the apartment. After a very tasty pizza we all went to bed early so that we would be ready for the next day. I'll write more tomorrow…..by James

19. Where was this passage most likely written ?
Tick ✓ the best answer.

A travel brochure ☐

A person's diary ☐

A newspaper ☐

A comic ☐

(5)

Do not write in this column

20. What time did the alarm clock ring at ?

( )

21. How many boys are in the family ?

( )

22. What short phrase explains why Mark was able to be helpful in the ski shop ?

( )

23. What was the weather like when they arrived in the ski resort ?

( )

Find the word in the passage that is closest in meaning to: -

24. a line of people ( )

25. small ( )

250g Washo Powder
£1.25

750g Washo Powder
£3.40

1kg Washo Powder
£4.10

26. Jill needs 3.25kgs to wash her clothes for a month. What is the cheapest way for her to buy this amount of "Washo Powder" ?
Tick ✓ the best answer.

13 boxes at 250g ☐

4 boxes at 750g and 1 box at 250g ☐

3 boxes a 1kg and 1 box at 250g ☐

2 boxes at 750g and 7 boxes at 250g ☐

(7)

Do not write in this column

27. Given the number fact that

£1.69 X 23 = £38.87

use this fact to answer this question.

£1.69 X 22 = (£______________)

28. A plane leaves London for New York at 1.00pm.
The time at New York is 5 hours behind London.
The flight lasts 5hours and 30 minutes.
What is the time in New York when the plane arrives ?
Tick ✓ the best answer.

6.30am ☐

1.30pm ☐

6.30pm ☐

1.30am ☐

29. Circle all the square numbers in the list below.

3 7 9 12 36 48 90

30. Calculate 75% of 824. (________________)

31. How many cuboids are in the shape drawn below ?

(____________ cuboids)

32. Paul is facing NE and he turns 180° clockwise and then 45° anticlockwise.
What direction is he now facing ?

(______________________)

(6)

Do not write in this column	

33. Look at this diagram of a boat on the sea. (The diagram is not drawn to scale.)
What is the total distance from the seabed to the very top of the boat ?

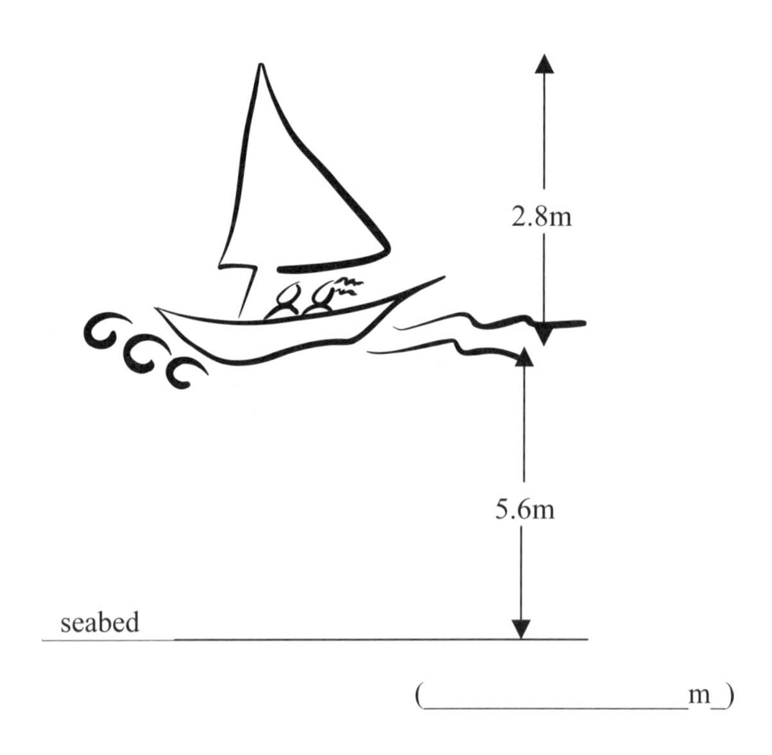

(________________m)

34. Geoff, Helen, Sandra and Michael play a game and keep their scores in a table.
The average score is 23. Complete the table by inserting Michael's score.

	SCORE
Geoff	**27**
Helen	**18**
Sandra	**35**
Michael	(____________)

35. What is the volume of a box measuring 3.7cm X 2.8cm X 10cm ?

(________________cm cubed)

36. Circle any two fractions that are equivalent.

$\frac{1}{2}$ $\frac{4}{5}$ $\frac{2}{3}$ $\frac{4}{9}$ $\frac{4}{8}$ $\frac{3}{2}$

(4)

Do not write in this column

Registration to use our Internet Services.

Thank you for applying to use the internet services for our appointment	(line 1)
booking and repeat prescription ordering service.	(line 2)
First time users – please follow the "create your account" link at the	(line 3)
top of the login page.	(line 4)
There are two more registration screens following this first screen. The	(line 5)
information that you enter on the first screen enables the system to check	(line 6)
your identity when you log on. On the second screen you enter a password	(line 7)
and security details that no-one else will know. This will then allow access	(line 8)
to the next screen.	(line 9)
The information that you need to complete your registration screen is	(line 10)
enclosed with your letter. Look after this letter carefully until you	(line 11)
register and then destroy it. If this letter is lost or stolen before you	(line 12)
have entered your password contact the surgery immediately, by	(line 13)
telephone or in person and we will issue new passwords.	(line 14)
Remember to enter your details and information exectly as they are	(line 15)
printed in your letter or your registration will not be accepted. When you	(line 16)
have registered and wish to use the system you must then also enter all	(line 17)
details in exactly the same format.	(line 18)
Thank you for using our new system.	(line 19)

37. What are first time users asked to do ?
Tick ✓ the best answer.

- Open a bank account ☐
- Go to the bank ☐
- Create their account ☐
- Count their money ☐

38. How many registration screens are there ?
Tick ✓ the best answer.

- One registration screen ☐
- Two registration screens ☐
- Three registration screens ☐
- Four registration screens ☐

(2)

Do not write in this column

39. There is a spelling error in one of the lines.
Which line is it ?
Tick ✓ the best answer.

Line 7 ☐

Line 10 ☐

Line 15 ☐

Line 19 ☐

40. The word **CHECK** is used at line 6.
What word from the list below means the same or almost the same as **CHECK** ?
Tick ✓ the best answer.

striped ☐

verify ☐

watch ☐

create ☐

41. Which sentence below uses speech marks correctly ?
Tick ✓ the best answer.

"Janet said," I would like to be a doctor. ☐

Janet said, I would like to be a "doctor." ☐

Janet said, "I would like to be a doctor." ☐

Janet "said," I would like to be a doctor. ☐

(3)

Do not write in this column
(4)

42. This pie chart and table show the same information about 90 school children and the pets that they own. Each pupil owns only one pet.

PET	NUMBER OF PUPILS
DOG	45
CAT	10
RABBIT	30
HAMSTER	10

C

D

A

B

Which section of the pie chart represents those pupils that own a **rabbit** ?
Tick ✓ the best answer.

Section A ☐

Section B ☐

Section C ☐

Section D ☐

43. A waitress pours 4 glasses of lemonade from a 1.5 litre bottle.
Each glass contains 330ml. How much lemonade is left in the bottle ?

(________________ml)

44. Look at this display on a calculator.

00191.02

Round this number to the nearest 10. (________________)

45. If I increase a certain number by one fifth I get 24 as my answer.
If I double that same certain number what is my answer ? (________________)

Do not write in this column

This table shows the cost of flights from Belfast to Rome and includes prices for adults, children and infants.

Date of Flight	**Adult fare**	**Child fare (upto 12 years at date of travel)**	**Infant fare (upto 2 years at date of travel)**
1 Jan – 30 April	£190	£120	FREE
1 May – 3 July	£280	£190	25% of adult fare
4 July – 30 Sept	£345	£260	40% of adult fare
1 Oct – 31 Dec	£220	£150	FREE

Use this information to calculate the following fares.

46. What is the total fare for 2 adults, a three year old child and an 18 month infant departing 5Th July ?

(£____________________)

47. What is the total fare for 3 adults and 18 month twin infants departing 3rd July ?

(£____________________)

48. How much more expensive is it for 2 adults to travel on the 1st May rather than the 30th April ?

(£____________________)

(3)

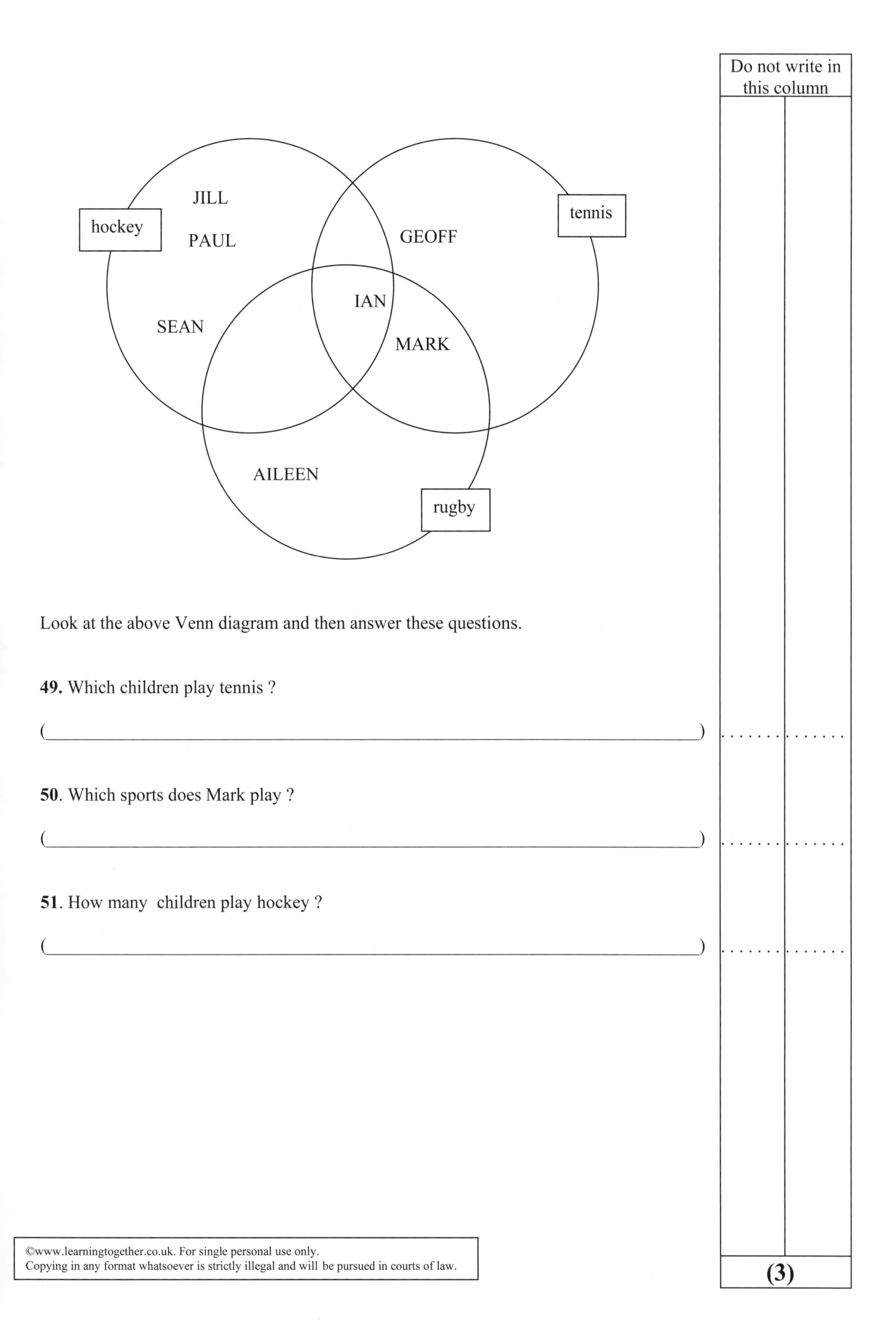

Look at the above Venn diagram and then answer these questions.

49. Which children play tennis ?

(____)

50. Which sports does Mark play ?

(____)

51. How many children play hockey ?

(____)

Do not write in this column

THE STORM

The wind howls as it passes by	**(line 1)**
Raindrops are flung against the window	**(line 2)**
So hard that they shudder and trickle down	**(line 3)**
The trees sway dangerously	**(line 4)**
Early daffodils lie limp and lifeless on the dark earth	**(line 5)**
The door slams with the force of the violent wind	**(line 6)**
The rain lashes down making puddles on the ground	**(line 7)**
There is no more sun – only a chilly breeze rising in the air	**(line 8)**
- maybe spring is over?	**(line 9)**

By Jill McConkey (aged 10)

52. The poet uses the word **flung** in the second line.
Which word means the same or almost the same as **flung** ?
Tick ✓ the best answer.

Flew ☐

Thrown ☐

Raining ☐

Windy ☐

53. What closes because of the wind ? (________________________)

54. Which type of flowers are mentioned in the poem ?

(____)

55. Circle the adjective in this sentence from the poem.

The door slams with the force of the violent wind

56. Why does the poet end the poem with a "?"
Tick ✓ the best answer.

She is asking the teacher a question ☐

She is asking the reader a question ☐

She is asking her mother a question ☐

She is asking the headmaster a question ☐

(5)

Do not write in this column

57. What phrase of up to six words tells the reader that the daffodils have finished blooming ?

(____)

58. Find one word in the sixth line that tells us that the wind has great strength.

(____)

(2)

ANSWERS TO LEARNING TOGETHER
Association of Quality Education Practice TEST NUMBER 1

1	Regal	**31**	18 cuboids
2	Nectar	**32**	South
3	The branches are coming to life after winter	**33**	8.4m
4	Gentle	**34**	12
5	Stands	**35**	103.6 cm cubed
6	sweet	**36**	1/2 4/8
7	Salmon, cherries, chairs	**37**	Create their account
8	2.1m	**38**	Three registration screens
9	1.15m	**39**	Line 15
10	21.2m	**40**	Verify
11	£3.75	**41**	Janet said, "I would like to be a doctor."
12	£5.85	**42**	Section D
13	£12.00	**43**	180 ml
14	10 boxes	**44**	190.00 or 190
15	9	**45**	40
16	64	**46**	£1088.00
17	208	**47**	£980.00
18	9.25	**48**	£180.00
19	A person's diary	**49**	Geoff, Ian, Mark
20	7.30	**50**	Tennis & Rugby
21	3	**51**	4
22	He had skied before (with his school)	**52**	Thrown
23	Snowing	**53**	The door
24	Queue	**54**	Daffodils
25	Compact	**55**	Violent
26	3 boxes a 1kg and 1 box at 250g	**56**	She is asking the reader a question
27	£37.18	**57**	Early daffodils lie limp and lifeless
28	1.30 pm	**58**	force
29	9, 36		
30	618		

Whilst the content of this test is believed to be true and accurate at the time of publishing, neither the authors nor the publishers can accept any legal responsibility or liability for any errors or omissions that may have been made.

ADVICE AND INSTRUCTIONS ON COMPLETING THIS TEST

Association of Quality Education Practice TEST NUMBER 2
Common Entrance Assessment Practice Paper

1. **There are 58 questions in this test.**
2. **Start at question 1 and work your way to question 58.**
3. **If you are unable to complete a question leave it and go to the next one.**
4. **Do not think about the question you have just left as this wastes time.**
5. **If you change an answer make sure the change is clear.**
6. **You may do any rough work on the test paper or on another piece of paper.**
7. **This test should take approximately 60 minutes.**
8. **When you have finished this test mark it with an adult.**
9. **An adult may be able to explain any questions you do not understand.**

Do not write in this column

ALL HALLOWS EVE

I hide behind the sofa quivering in fear
Now the witching hour is near
The curtains are drawn tight
And I've turned off the lights
The TV volume is way down low
I sit and cower in its feeble glow
Then comes the knock upon the door
And I curl up quivering on the floor
My heart is pounding my breath is shallow
My mouth is dry it's hard to swallow
On all hallows eve I live in mortal dread
But not of monsters or the un-dead
The fear that turns my heart to stone
Is Trick or Treaters knowing I'm home

(Poem courtesy of www.funny-poems.co.uk)

1. The poet uses the phrase **"My heart is pounding."**
Why does he use this phrase ?
Tick ☐ the best answer.

- Because he has been running ☐
- His heart is breaking ☐
- He is afraid ☐
- He has found a pound coin ☐

2. What is dry ?

(____)

3. The poet uses the phrase **"I sit and cower in its feeble glow."**
What has a feeble glow ?
Tick ✓ the best answer.

- The moon ☐
- The stars ☐
- The TV ☐
- The streetlights ☐

(3)

Do not write in this column	

4. Which phrase of two or three words let us know that the curtains are closed ?

(____)

5. Which phrase of five words let us know that the poet is frightened on All Hallows Eve ?

(____)

6. In this poem what is the poet letting us know about his feelings ?
   Tick ✓ the best answer.

   He is sad ☐

   He is tired ☐

   He is old ☐

   He is frightened ☐

7. Circle the verb in this line from the poem.

My mouth is dry it's hard to swallow

8. Calculate 70% of 400. (________________)

9. Calculate 60% of £ 6.50. (____£__________)

10. Calculate X if X + 18 = 50 (________________)

11. Calculate X if X + 12 = 16. (________________)

(8)

Do not write in this column

12. If 4 buns cost 60p how much would 7 buns cost ? (£__________)

13. If 6 toys cost £48 how much would 10 toys cost ? (£__________)

14. What is the probability of throwing a 3 on a die?
Tick ✓ the best answer.

- 1 in 1 ☐
- 1 in 6 ☐
- 2 in 3 ☐
- 3 in 4 ☐

Complete this table by changing the times to 12 or 24 hour clocks as necessary.
(Use am or pm as required)

	12 hour clock	24 hour
15	9.15 am.	
16		17:25
17		23:10
18	3.25pm.	

(7)

Do not write in this column	
....	....
....	....
(2)	

Introducing the NEW Patio Power Plus

New Patio Power Plus is a new version of one of our previous accessory products, namely Patio Power Cleaner. Goclean was the first to introduce a Patio cleaner.

The new Patio Power Plus is a particularly effective cleaner unit designed for use on large flat areas, such as paving stones, driveways, terraces, walls and fences. A new feature on this model is a special regulator that lets you adjust the water pressure to suit each individual job.

This eliminates unwanted splashes or spray. This accessory is fitted with two handles, which make sure it is always easy to use, regardless of whether you are right-handed or left-handed. These handles can also be adjusted to make it even easier to clean vertical surfaces, such as fences or walls.

New Compact pressure washer The C 120.4

New Compact cold water pressure washer is an add on to the Goclean Compact range of pressure washers for 2018, and now features a design with a more robust, masculine appearance. The 2018 model is intended for consumers, who on occasions need a high pressure cleaner for cleaning jobs in and around the home. This new model is fitted with the ergonomically correct G8 sprayer handle, which makes it very comfortable to use.

This cleaner is extremely robust and long lasting. For example, the pump is made of aluminium. The New Compact is an effective high pressure cleaner that is both small and handy. A spray gun with the Goclean quick coupling, for easy fitting to the hose, is included as standard. All models are also fitted with the Click and Pull nozzle system, which enables you to change accessories quickly and easily.

The New Compact is part of the overall range of Goclean high-pressure cleaners.

The Excellent range is intended for consumers who make frequent use of high pressure cleaning equipment, while the Pro range is designed for semi-professional users.

19. Where was this passage most likely written ?
Tick ✓ the best answer.

A company brochure ☐

A travel magazine ☐

A novel ☐

A letter to a friend ☐

20. How many handles does the Patio Power Plus have ?

(________________)

Do not write in this column

Find the word in the second paragraph that is closest in meaning to: -

21. works very well (________________________)

Find the word in the third paragraph that is closest in meaning to: -

22. altered to suit (________________________)

23. What new feature of the Patio Power Plus helps "eliminate unwanted splashes or spray" ?

(____)

24. In the C 120.4 model what is the pump made of ?

(____)

25. What new feature of the Patio Power Plus makes it easier to clean vertical surfaces ?

(____)

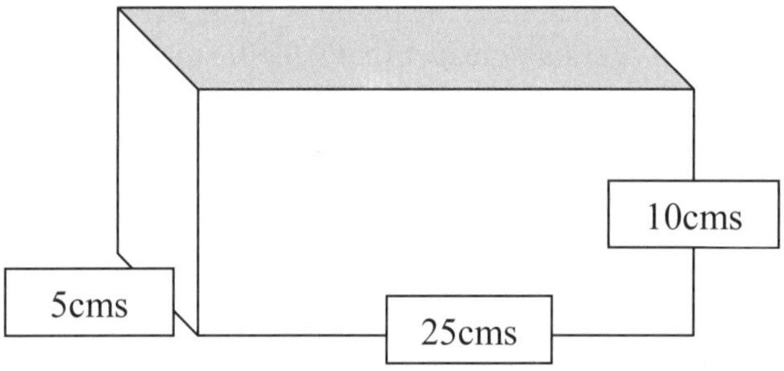

10cms

5cms

25cms

26. Calculate the volume of the above shape.
(The shape is not drawn to scale.)

(______________________cm3__)

27. Circle the number in which the 3 stands for 30.

304.0 **13.28** **3176.09** **138.6** **57.30**

28. A ¼ of a number plus 6 equals 10. What is that number? (____________________)

(8)

Do not write in this column	
(4)	

29. Look at this equation and decide what answer goes in the brackets.
Tick ✓ the best answer.

8 x 40 = (___?___) x 80

20 ☐

15 ☐

4 ☐

160 ☐

30. Look at this equation and decide what answer goes in the brackets.
Tick ✓ the best answer.

18 x 6 = 36 x (__?___)

3 ☐

9 ☐

72 ☐

24 ☐

What number does the arrow point to on these number lines?

31. (__________)

32. (__________)

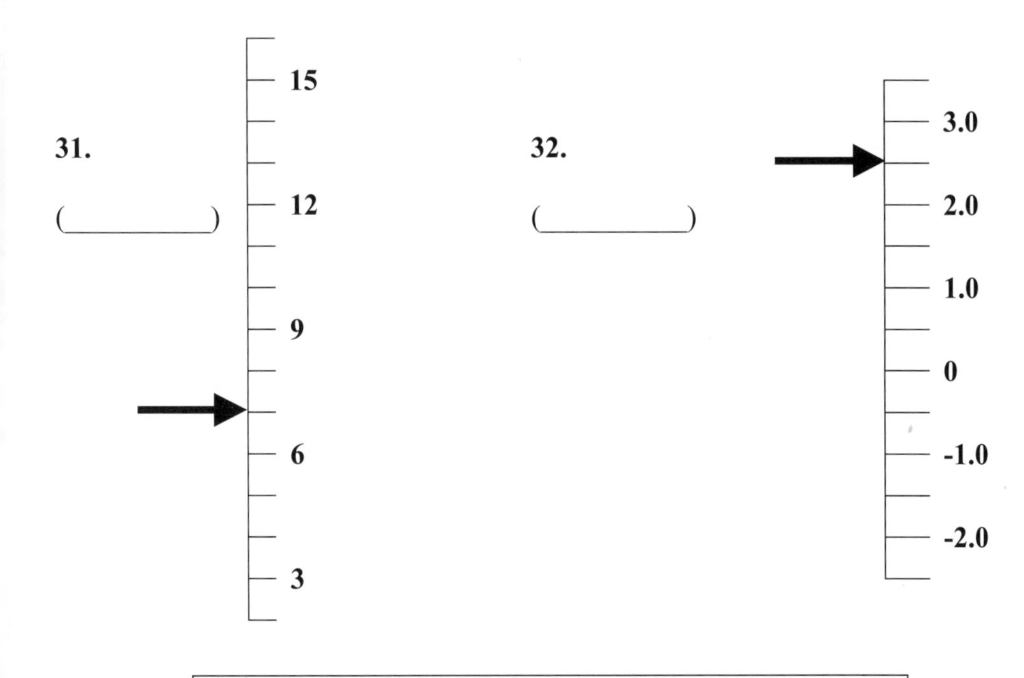

Do not write in this column

33. The temperature at midday was 12°C. By midnight it had dropped by 14°C.
What was the temperature at midnight?

(______ ________°____)

34. A bicycle costing £120 is reduced by 25%.
What is the new cost?

(___£__ ______________)

35. Calculate $\frac{4}{5}$ of 125. (____________________)

36. Look at the information in the table about which countries each pupil has visited.
Enter the same information into the Venn diagram.

Pupil's name	Spain	Italy	France
Paul	YES	NO	YES
Janet	NO	NO	YES
Jill	YES	YES	YES
Nick	YES	NO	NO

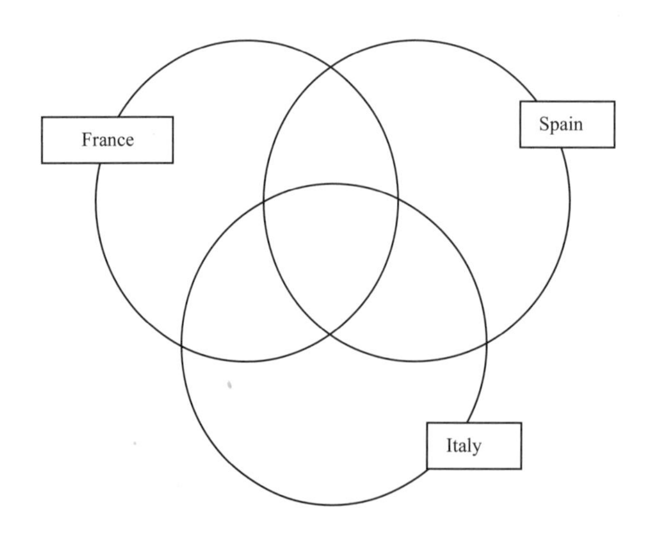

(4)

Do not write in this column	
(1)	

David Robert Joseph Beckham (OBE)

David, who was born 2 May 1975, is an English footballer who currently (line 1)
plays in midfield for Italian club Milan. He is on loan from an American (line 2)
club called Los Angeles Galaxy and he has played many times for the (line 3)
England national team. Beckham's stint with Milan began on 7 January 2009. (line 4)

He was twice runner-up for FIFA World Player of the Year and in 2004 (line 5)
he was thought to be the world's highest-paid footballer. Beckham is the (line 6)
first British footballer to play 100 Champions League matches. He is (line 7)
known throughout the world and was the most searched of all sports stars (line 8)
in both 2003 and 2004 on the Google computer search engine. With such (line 9)
global recognition he has become an elite advertising brand and a top (line 10)
fashion icon. Beckham captained England in the 2006 FIFA World Cup (line 11)
finals and has recently gained his hundredth selection for England. He is (line 12)
currently England's most-capped outfield player. (line 13)

Beckham's career began when he signed a professional contract with (line 14)
Manchester United, making his first-team debut in 1992 aged 17. During (line 15)
his time there, United won the Premier League title six times, the FA Cup (line 16)
twice and they also won the UEFA Champions League in 1999. He left (line 17)
Manchester United to play for Spanish side Real Madrid in 2003. He remained (line 18)
there for four seasons. (line 19)

In January 2007, it was announced that Beckham would leaf Real Madrid (line 20)
and he signed a five-year contract with American club Los Angeles Galaxy. (line 21)
He joined his new club on 1 July 2007 and he immediately became the (line 22)
highest paid player in American soccer history. (line 23)

Beckham is married to Victoria Beckham who is a former member of the (line 24)
group “Spice Girls.” (line 25)

The couple have three sons and currently reside in Beverly Hills, California (line 26)

37. According to the report above where does David Beckham play football now ?
Tick ✓ the best answer.

England ☐

Milan ☐

Los Angeles ☐

Madrid ☐

Do not write in this column

38. Using the information in the report decide how many times he has played for England ?
Tick ✓ the best answer.

At least 100 times ☐

90 times ☐

More than 100 times ☐

120 times ☐

39. There is a spelling error in one of the lines.
Which line is it ?
Tick ✓ the best answer.

Line 3 ☐

Line 20 ☐

Line 18 ☐

Line 19 ☐

40. Which phrase of two words used between line 7 and line 13 tells us that he is known throughout the world ?

(____)

41. Which word used between line 20 and line 26 means the same or almost the same as **"used to belong to." ?**

Tick ✓ the best answer.

signed ☐

former ☐

contract ☐

reside ☐

(4)

Do not write in this column	

42. This is a right-angled triangle.
Angle C is 30°   What size is Angle A ?   (__________ °)

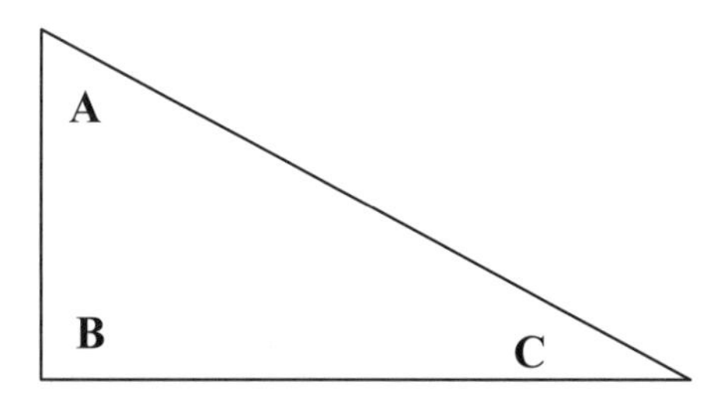

43. Complete the table below.

Shapes	Edges	Vertices	Faces
Cube	12	(_______)	6
Triangular prism	(_______)	6	5
Square based pyramid	8	5	(_______)

44. Each square in this diagram measures 1 cm by 1cm.
Look at the grey shape and calculate its area in cm^2

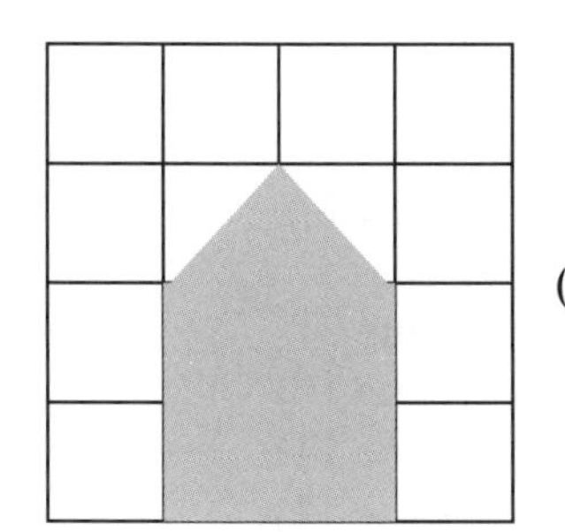

(________________ cm^2 _____)

x = 3   **a = 7**   **y = 5**   **b = 4**   **n = 2**

Use the information above to work out the following equations.

45. x + y + b = (__________)   **46.** 2a – n = (__________)

(5)

Do not write in this column

47. How much change will I have from £50 after buying 3 books at £6 each and 2 C.D.s at £11.50 each? (___£________________)

48. What is a quarter of 40 divided by 2 ? (____________________)

49. How many days from 14th July until 17th August (inclusive) ?

(________________days__)

50. A man rules a line on a page using a scale of 1cm. to 15km. His line is 4cm.long. What length does this represent in real life ?

(_________________km_)

51. 420 x 24 = (________________) x 4

Aunts

You mustn't be fooled by their features.	**(Line 1)**
They look sweet, and kind, and gentle,	**(Line 2)**
Some would say quite ornamental,	**(Line 3)**
But they're really scary creatures.	**(Line 4)**
'Come here and have a great big hug'	**(Line 5)**
She squeezes me 'til I can't speak,	**(Line 6)**
Then kisses me upon the cheek,	**(Line 7)**
Saliva, lipstick, perfume ugh!	**(Line 8)**
It's Christmas time I really fear.	**(Line 9)**
It's just the same year after year,	**(Line 10)**
As I unwrap my worst knightmare,	**(Line 11)**
A set of knitted underwear.	**(Line 12)**
So this year I thought I'd treat her	**(Line 13)**
To a gift which she could treasure	**(Line 14)**
And would give me equal pleasure.	**(Line 15)**
I've bought her a Spiny Aunteater	**(Line 16)**

(Poem courtesy of www.funny-poems.co.uk)

(5)

Do not write in this column	

52. There is a spelling error in one of the lines. Which line is it ?
Tick ✓ the best answer.

- Line 13 ☐
- Line 11 ☐
- Line 1 ☐
- Line 8 ☐

53. From the information given in the poem who or what are the **"scary creatures"** ?

(____)

54. What three things are left on the poet's cheek ?

(____)

55. What is the poet's worst nightmare ?
Tick ✓ the best answer.

- A set of knitted underwear. ☐
- Spiders ☐
- The darkness ☐
- Spines of anteaters ☐

56. Why time of year does the poet fear most ?

(____)

57. What phrase of up to seven words tells the reader that the poet's aunt hugs him tightly ?

(____)

58. Find one word in the last verse that means the same or almost he same as "enjoyment."

(____)

(7)

ANSWERS TO LEARNING TOGETHER
Association of Quality Education Practice TEST NUMBER 2

1	He is afraid	**31**	7
2	His mouth	**32**	2.5
3	The TV	**33**	-2
4	(are) drawn tight	**34**	£90.00
5	I live in mortal dread	**35**	100
6	He is frightened	**36**	See bottom of page
7	swallow	**37**	Milan
8	280	**38**	At least 100 times
9	£3.90	**39**	Line 20
10	32	**40**	global recognition
11	4	**41**	former
12	£1.05	**42**	60°
13	£80.00	**43**	(Cube) 8 (Tri Prism) 9 (Sq Based Prism) 5
14	1 in 6	**44**	$5cm^2$
15	09.15	**45**	12
16	5.25pm	**46**	12
17	11.10pm	**47**	£9.00
18	15.25	**48**	5
19	A company brochure	**49**	35 days
20	2	**50**	60km
21	effective	**51**	2520
22	adjusted	**52**	Line 11
23	A special regulator	**53**	aunts
24	aluminium	**54**	saliva, lipstick, perfume
25	(adjustable) handles	**55**	A set of knitted underwear
26	$1250cm^3$	**56**	Christmas
27	138.6	**57**	She squeezes me 'til I can't speak
28	16	**58**	pleasure
29	4		
30	3		

France
Spain
Paul
Nick
Janet
Jill
Italy

ADVICE AND INSTRUCTIONS ON COMPLETING THIS TEST

Association of Quality Education Practice TEST NUMBER 3
Common Entrance Assessment Practice Paper

1. **There are 58 questions in this test.**
2. **Start at question 1 and work your way to question 58.**
3. **If you are unable to complete a question leave it and go to the next one.**
4. **Do not think about the question you have just left as this wastes time.**
5. **If you change an answer make sure the change is clear.**
6. **You may do any rough work on the test paper or on another piece of paper.**
7. **This test should take approximately 60 minutes.**
8. **When you have finished this test mark it with an adult.**
9. **An adult may be able to explain any questions you do not understand.**

Whilst the content of this test is believed to be true and accurate at the time of publishing, neither the authors nor the publishers can accept any legal responsibility or liability for any errors or omissions that may have been made. If, however, you do find any errors please contact us at learningtogether@nireland.com so that we can correct them.

Do not write in this column

Eat, Drink and Be Messy

Once, upon a thyme leaf,
There lived a lazy snail,
Who munched and dozed, and dozed and munched,
On thyme he breakfasted and lunched,

And when it came to half past nine,
He chose once more to dine on thyme.
Later, upon the thyme leaf,
Was a rather plumper snail.

But, reader dear, his life was brief,
For this is no fairy tale.
He ate more and more, and grew fatter and fatter
Until one day he exploded, bang, splat, splatter.

One minute he was there,
The next he'd gone.
The coroner's verdict
'A snail thyme bomb'.

(Poem courtesy of www.funny-poems.co.uk)

1. Where did the snail live ?
Tick ✓ the best answer.

In the grass ☐

On a leaf ☐

In a garden ☐

On a breakfast plate ☐

2. What word in the third verse tells the reader that the snail's life was short ?

(____)

3. Using the information in the poem decide what word best describes one charactaristic of the snail ?
Tick ✓ the best answer.

Hard working ☐

Slimy ☐

Greedy ☐

Noisy ☐

(3)

Do not write in this column	
......	......
......	......
......	......
......	......
......	......
......	......
......	......
......	......
(9)	

4. Circle one verb in this line from the poem.

He chose once more to dine on thyme

5. Find one word in the last verse that means the same or almost he same as **"decision."**

(____)

6. What phrase of two words tells the reader that the snail has died ?

(____)

7. Circle the pronoun in this line from the poem.

He chose once more to dine on thyme.

8. What is the area of a right-angled triangle with short sides of 12cm and 6cm ?

(______________ cm^2 _)

9. A man spends £3.15, £5.85 and £7.50 in a restaurant.
How much does he spend altogether ?

(£______________)

10. If one coat costs £22.50 how much will 8 coats cost ? (£______________)

11. Calculate X if $X + 12 = 36$. (______________)

12. What fraction of this shape is shaded ?

(______________)

13. A block of ice-cream weighs 26.4g.
What would 5 blocks weigh ? (______________g__)

14. Turning clockwise, how many degrees are between 3 and 5 on a clock face ?

(______________ $^\circ$)

15. 16 x 84 = 32 x (______________)

16. What is the value of the underlined and **bold** digit in each of the following numbers ?

E.g. 5**3**4 ⟶ **30** 10**2** ⟶ **2**

3**6**71 (______________)

29**4**6 (______________)

Look at the shape drawn below and then answer questions **17** and **18**.

17. What is the volume of this shape that is not drawn to scale ? (______________m^3_)

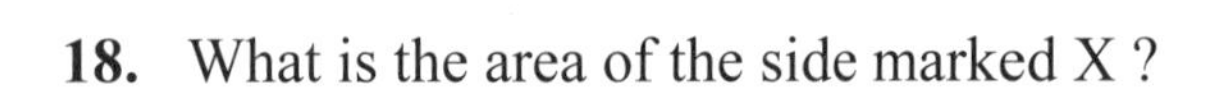

18. What is the area of the side marked X ? (______________m^2_)

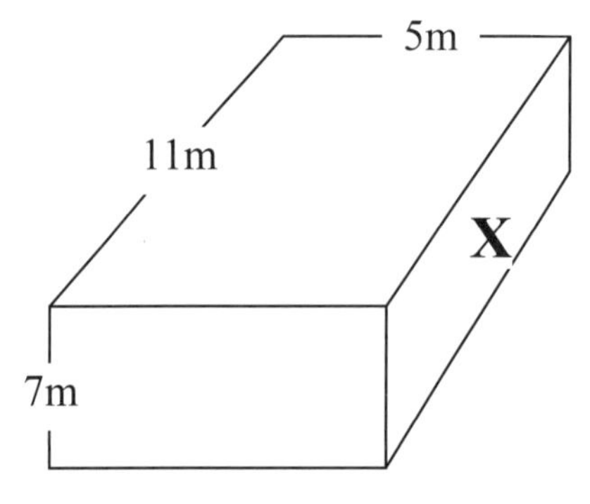

(6)

Do not write in this column

The Mountains of Mourne.

The Mournes, as they are usually known, are visited by many thousands of tourists, hillwalkers, cyclists and rock climbers. Following a fundraising drive in 1993, the National Trust purchased nearly 5.3 km^2 (1,300 acres) of land in the Mournes. This included a part of Slieve Donard and nearby Slieve Commedagh, at 767 metres (2,520 ft) the second-highest mountain in the area.

The Mourne Wall is among the more famous features in the Mournes. It is a 35 kilometres long dry-stone wall that crosses fifteen summits, constructed to define the boundaries of the 36 square kilometres (8,900 acres) area of land purchased by the Belfast Water Commissioners in the late 1800s.

This followed a number of Acts of Parliament allowing the sale, and the establishment of a water supply from the Mournes to what was then the growing industrial city of Belfast. Construction of the Mourne Wall was started in 1904 and was completed in 1922.

Many of the mountains have names beginning ***Slieve***, from the Irish word ***sliabh***, meaning ***mountain***. As well as many of the well-known mountains such as Slieve Donard, Slieve Lamagan and Slieve Muck, there are a number of other curious names: Pigeon Rock; Buzzard's Roost; Brandy Pad; the Cock and Hen; Percy Bysshe; the Devil's Coach Road and Pollaphuca, which means "hole of the fairies or sprites".

The Mournes are very popular as a destination for many young people who are taking part in their Duke of Edinburgh's Award expeditions.

The Mournes were said to be the inspiration for C.S. Lewis' magical world of Narnia.

19. Why was the dry stone wall built ?
Tick ✓ the best answer.

To keep the sheep in ☐

To protect people from the wind ☐

To show the boundary of the Water Commissioners land ☐

To use old bricks ☐

20. What are the Mountains more usually called ?

(____________________)

21. What word as used in the third paragraph means the same or almost the same as **"to build something"** ?

(____________________)

(3)

Do not write in this column	

22. Which name means **"Hole of the Spirits"**
Tick ✓ the best answer.

Percy Bysshe ☐

Buzzard's Roost ☐

Pollaphuca ☐

Brandy Pad ☐

23. In what year was a lot of money raised to buy part of the Mountains of Mourne ?

(________________)

The author uses apostrophes in the passage. They can be used to show ownership or to show that letters have been left out in a word and the word has been shortened.

In these questions the apostrophes have been used to shorten words.

Write the full words in each case

Eg they're (they are)

24. we're (____________________________)

I'll (____________________________)

25. Can't (____________________________)

won't (____________________________)

Round these numbers to the nearest 10.

26. 23 (______) 256 (______) 591 (______) 1003 (________)

27. Find the average of these numbers.

17 39 35 25 (__________________)

(6)

Place	July	August	September	October
B	11.2	9.4	9.8	12.0
C	10.3	9.9	7.4	10.6
D	9.1	7.7	8.7	14.7
R	6.9	5.1	9.4	12.7
S	8.6	12.9	12.9	15.7

The above table shows the rainfall in cms at five places, called B, C, D, R and S, in each of the months July, August, September and October.

28. Which place has the most rainfall in the month of September ?

(________________)

29. Which place has the least rainfall during the month of July ?

(________________)

This timetable shows the time when 5 shops are open:

A	8.15a.m. to 4.30p.m.
B	8.45a.m. to 5.15p.m.
C	8.30a.m. to 4.45p.m.
D	9.10a.m. to 5.30p.m.
E	9.15a.m. to 5.00p.m.

30. Which shop is open for the longest time ? (________)

31. Which shop is open for the shortest time ? (________)

32. How much longer is shop D open than shop E ? (____________)

33. How many faces does a square based pyramid have? (__________ Faces)

34. **Given that** **a = 6** **b = 5** **c = 3**

Find the value of: -

5b + 2c = (________)

35. **Given that** **a = 6** **b = 5** **c = 3**

Find the value of: -

a X c = (________)

36. If the fourth day of a month is Tuesday, then what date will the third Thursday of the month be ?

(______________)

Do not write in this column

(9)

Do not write in this column

Google Inc. Search engine

Google is an American public corporation, earning revenue from advertising (Line 1)
related to its Internet search engine. Google also sells versions of the same (Line 2)
technologies but without advertising. The Google headquarters, the Googleplex, (Line 3)
is located in Mountain View, California. At March 31, 2009, the company (Line 4)
had 20,164 full-time employees. (Line 5)

Google was co-founded by Larry Page and Sergey Brin while they were (Line 6)
both students at Stanford University. The company was first listed as a (Line 7)
privately held company on September 4, 1998. In 2004 the company offered (Line 8)
shares on the stock market and the first shares were sold on August 19, 2004. (Line 9)
This sale raised US$1.67 billion. (Line 10)

Google has continued its growth through producing a series of new products (Line 11)
and by buying other companies. Environmentalism, giving money to charity (Line 12)
and positive employee relations have been important building blocks during (Line 13)
the growth of Google. (Line 14)

The company is so good to its employees that it has been identified (Line 15)
multiple times as Fortune Magazine's Number 1 "Best Place to Work." The (Line 16)
unofficial company slogan is "Don't be evil." Google has been criticised (Line 17)
regarding the privacy of personal information that it receives and about (Line 18)
discontinuation of services, which means that the public must buy the new (Line 19)
product. According to Millward Brown, (a research company), it is the (Line 20)
most powerful brand in the world. (Line 21)

37. Lines **20** and **21** state that Millward Brown thinks that Google is the world's most powerful brand.
Who or what is Millward Brown ?
Tick ✓ the best answer.

He owns Google ☐

He works for Google ☐

It is a research company ☐

A town in California ☐

38. What is the Google headquarters called ?

(______________)

39. What word in line **1** means the same or almost the same as **"earnings"** ?

(______________)

(3)

Do not write in this column

40. Companies in line **12** is the plural of company.
What is the plural of these words.

box (____________________)

turkey (____________________)

calf (____________________)

deer (____________________)

41. Circle the adjective in this extract from the passage about Google.

.....which means that the public must buy the new product.

42. Beside each angle write its correct name e.g. acute, obtuse or reflex.

95° (________________) 64° (________________) 210° (________________)

43. Some of the nets below will fold into a cube.
Put a circle around all of those nets **that will fold** to make a cube.

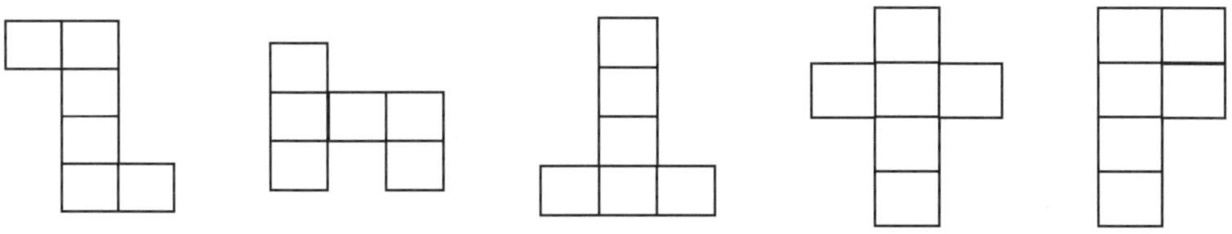

A B C D E

44. If one millilitre of water weighs one gram, how much does a litre weigh ?

(________________g)

45. A clock strikes the number of hours and once every half hour. How many times does it strike altogether between 12.25pm and 3.05 pm ?

(________________)

46. A suit is reduced in the sale by 25%. If the original cost was £180, how much does the suit cost in the sale ?

(__£________________)

(7)

Do not write in this column

47. What is the volume of a cube whose height is 5cm ? (______________ cm^3 __)

48. What is a fifth of 60 divided by 3 ? (____________________)

49. Share 15 apples between Janet and Jill so that for every **THREE** apples Janet gets Jill gets **TWO** apples.

How many apples does Janet get? (____________________)

50. Circle the most likely answer.
A human walking normally will walk at about:

1mph 12mph 3mph 8mph 16mph 32mph

51. A factory should have 468 workers. There are only 419 at the moment.
How many more can be employed?

(____________________)

Ballooning

Of all the pastimes
Which defy all logic
Hot air ballooning
Must be the most fantastic
You take off
With no controls to ponder
At the mercy of the wind
Into the great blue yonder
Floating up and away
Heart fit to blow a gasket
Gripping the hand rail
And stood in a picnic basket
A Bunsen burner flames
Under a piece of fabric
Hot air ballooning
Must be the most fantastic.

(Poem courtesy of www.funny-poems.co.uk)

52. What phrase of up to six words tells the reader that the wind controls the balloon ?

(____)

(6)

Do not write in this column	

53. Which word from the poem means the same or almost the same as **"to think about something"** ?

Tick ✓ the best answer.

Fabric ☐

Ponder ☐

Defy ☐

Gasket ☐

54. What is the **"piece of fabric"** mentioned in the poem ?

(____________)

55. The poet uses rhyming words in the poem.
From the list below choose a word that rhymes with each of the following.
Write the rhyming word in the brackets. Not all words are needed.

WAIT HAM LACK VIEW TRAY BEE LIAR

CHOIR (________________)

FREIGHT (________________)

QUEUE (________________)

56. Circle the **noun** in this line from the poem ?

With no controls to ponder

57. Which word from the poem means the same or almost the same as **"hobbies"** ?

(____________)

58. Circle any **adjective** in this line from the poem ?

Into the great blue yonder

(6)

ANSWERS TO LEARNING TOGETHER TEST NUMBER 3
Practice for Association of Quality Education Transfer Test

1	On a leaf	**31**	E
2	brief	**32**	35 mins
3	greedy	**33**	5 faces
4	chose / dine	**34**	31
5	verdict	**35**	18
6	he'd gone	**36**	20th
7	He	**37**	It is a research company
8	$36\ cm^2$	**38**	Googleplex
9	£16.50	**39**	revenue
10	£180.00	**40**	boxes, turkeys, calves, deer
11	24	**41**	new
12	½	**42**	obtuse, acute, reflex
13	132g	**43**	A & C & D
14	60°	**44**	1000g
15	42	**45**	9
16	600 , 40	**46**	£135.00
17	$385\ m^3$	**47**	$125\ cm^2$
18	$77\ m^2$	**48**	4
19	To show the boundary of the Water commissioners land	**49**	9
20	The Mournes	**50**	3 mph
21	Construction	**51**	49
22	Pollaphuca	**52**	At the mercy of the wind
23	1993	**53**	Ponder
24	We are , I will	**54**	The balloon
25	Can not , will not	**55**	Liar, wait, view
26	20 , 260 , 590 , 1000	**56**	controls
27	29	**57**	pastimes
28	S	**58**	great blue
29	R		
30	B		

Whilst the content of this test is believed to be true and accurate at the time of publishing, neither the authors nor the publishers can accept any legal responsibility or liability for any errors or omissions that may have been made.